The Synagogue Speaks

We thank our sponsors for their
generous support of this publication.

U.S. Institute of Museum and Library Services

David and Barbara B. Hirschhorn Foundation

Paul Mark Sandler, Esq.
Leslie Sandler
Gilbert Sandler

Ruth Marder

In Loving Memory of
Fay and Nathan Holzman
and Esther Ann Brown Adler

The Maryland Historical Trust

Additional support is provided by:
Maryland State Arts Council; Betsey and
Philip Kahn Publications Endowment;
Louis and Frances B. Booke Research
Endowment; and THE ASSOCIATED:
Jewish Community Federation of Baltimore.

Book design by PJ Bogert Graphic Design

Manufactured in the United States of America

The Jewish Museum of Maryland
15 Lloyd Street
Baltimore, MD 21202
410-732-6400
www.jewishmuseummd.org

The Jewish Museum of Maryland is an agency of
THE ASSOCIATED: Jewish Community Federation of Baltimore.

This publication has been financed in part with state funds from
the Maryland Historical Trust Historical and Cultural Museum
Assistance Program of the Maryland Department of Planning.
However, the contents and opinions do not necessarily reflect
the view or policies of the Trust, the Program, or the Maryland
Department of Planning.

The Synagogue Speaks

Pictures by Jonathon Scott Fuqua

Story by Anita Kassof

In Memory of Edward B. Sandler

President of the Jewish Historical Society of Maryland, 1987 - 1989

Long before your grandparents' grandparents were babies, before they walked or talked or tied their own shoes, I was built with shovel and pail, hammer and nail, brick and stone.

Long before skyscrapers were built or cars were invented, back when people traveled by horse and carriage, I rose from the ground.

I was a synagogue, new and proud.

On the day I opened my doors, people gathered around me to celebrate.

Babies the size of challah loaves bawled in their mothers' arms. Children held their fathers' sleeves. Blinking in the sunlight, they stood on tip-toe to see above the crowd.

Down the street came a parade. Men in long coats and tall black hats carried the Torah scrolls high and sang joyous songs. Husbands and wives, grandmas and grandpas, boys and girls, followed the scrolls inside.

When everyone was quiet, important men made long speeches. I heard English and Hebrew and even German that day. The families of Baltimore Hebrew Congregation—for that is who had built me—had sailed across the ocean from Germany to live in America.

Everyone talked about how handsome I was and what a fine place for Baltimore's Jews to gather and pray, study and sing, listen and learn.

Up in the balcony, women sat, backs straight, in my smooth wooden pews. Next to them children squirmed, struggling to be still as they listened to their fathers at their prayers below:

"*Baruch ata Adonai ...*"

"Blessed are you, O, Lord ..."

I remember Louis and Martin, mischievous boys
who squirmed the most. Sweet, serious Sarah, wrapping
her arms around her little sister Rosi, with the long
brown braids and shy brown eyes.

For many years, those children and their friends
and cousins and brothers and sisters played and laughed,
listened and learned, ran and wiggled, until the sunshine
coming from their smiles was as bright as the rays of
sunlight streaming through my windows.

Surely, I was the happiest building in town.

My pews were filled with people,

and I was filled with joy.

My families grew and grew. Soon I became so crowded that I grew too. Workmen came back with shovel and pail, hammer and nail, brick and stone to make me longer and larger.

When the workmen were nearly done, they attached ropes and chains to my stained glass window with its colorful Star of David. And then they turned the huge winch—*crank, creak, crank, creak*—so that the window rose into the air!

Jonas and Julia, Bernhard and Betsy stepped outside from the basement schoolroom and watched, eyes wide. The window climbed higher and higher, wobbled, slipped, caught … and fit in the big round hole in the wall. It sparkled and winked in the sunlight as if to say, "I am here to stay!" The children cheered and clapped until their teacher, skirts flapping, shooed them back downstairs.

Those laughing, tumbling children brought
me much joy. They stayed friendly and true.
But their parents began to argue, their angry
voices filling my rooms and rattling my windows.
　　"Women should not be permitted
　　　　to sing in the choir with the men!"
　　"Raising our voices together in song
　　　　　honors our religion!"
　　"No, we must honor our religion
　　　　by praying the same way our ancestors
　　　　　　have done for hundreds of years!"
　　"We are in America now, and we must
　　　　change with the times in this new land!"

One day, the quarrels grew so bad that a group of men stormed out of my front door, never to return. They built themselves a new synagogue, just down the street from me. They named it Chizuk Amuno.

I am sorry to say that it was many years before I could look down the street without feeling sad. But finally my new neighbor and I became friends. People prayed differently there, but not so differently. Just like my families, they started their prayers with those familiar words:

"*Baruch ata Adonai ...*"

"Blessed are you, O, Lord ..."

Slowly my families began to grow again. And then a big day
arrived. Horse carts drew up out front, carrying strange metal
pipes. Max and Minna stopped playing on my front steps and
came inside to watch as workers carried the pipes carefully
up the narrow stairs to my balcony. What could they be doing?

One by one, just so, they stood those pipes high
and fastened them tight. And when they
were done, they had built an organ!

For many years, my families gathered
to pray and sing, and the deep, rich organ
sang right along with them. Jonas and
Julia, Bernhard and Betsy grew up and got
married and had children of their own.
They brought them back, little bundles
in white lace, to gaze up with their bright
baby eyes at my stained glass window.

My pews were filled with people,
and I was filled with joy.

I thought things would go on like that forever.
How foolish I was!

One by one, my families moved away
to a fancier neighborhood with taller houses and
bigger trees. Their children went along with them,
eager to play in the great, green, grassy park nearby.

Then one day men came to take the Torah
scrolls away. Slowly, they walked down my aisle for
the last time and locked my tall doors behind them.

How I hoped they would come back! But
the next morning no one came. My rooms sat
silent and empty.

I was a synagogue, all alone.

What was to become of me?
Downstairs, the water in my ritual baths
grew dull and stale. Upstairs, dust floated
in the sunshine and settled on my pews.

Just when I'd almost stopped hoping, someone climbed my lonely front steps.

I heard people talking in a strange language. They had sailed across the ocean from Lithuania, and they wanted to make me into a church.

The new families called themselves St. John the Baptist Catholic Church. Now they had their own place to gather and pray, study and sing, listen and learn.

They built a handsome altar and a pulpit for the priest. Here and there, they placed statues of saints. They filled a font with water and lit candles and incense.

I was a church, new once again.

Oh, what joy the new children of St. John's brought me. There was blond-haired Ella, always asking questions. Her older brother John, so quiet and smart, sometimes helped the priest at the altar.

And Leonas, who loved to pull his little sister's hat off her head as she listened to the priest's deep voice fill the church.

"*In nominee Patris* ..."

"In the name of the Father ..."

One day, workmen climbed up,
up, up onto my roof and
built a tower on top.
My families placed a
shiny new bell on the altar and
surrounded it with flowers. And the
Cardinal came and blessed that bell.
John and Ella were invited to
stand on the altar with the Cardinal. John was proud
to be there, but Ella just whispered and fidgeted.
One look from the priest, though, and she was quiet.
Workmen put the bell in the tower on the
roof and every day, a man pulled on a thick rope
and rang it—clang, clang, clang! The bell called
people to gather and pray and sing inside me.
The organ sang right along with them.
My pews were filled with people,
and I was filled with joy.

The families of St. John's made me feel young again. They gave my outside a fresh coat of warm red paint. And they built stairs, two sets. Pretty soon those steps were polished to a shine by the happy feet of Josef and Jurgis, Matas and Maria, as they ran and skipped up and down, down and up.

Upstairs, families celebrated Mass:

"*In nominee Patris …*"

"In the name of the Father …"'

Downstairs, they celebrated after baptisms and weddings, they ate and danced. Once they even showed a movie. Elizabeta and Aleks, Karol and Tomas huddled in the shadows, fascinated by the grainy black and white pictures projected on the wall.

I thought things would

go on like that forever.

And then it happened again.

My families grew so much they could no longer
fit inside of me. They needed a bigger place
to gather and pray, study and sing, listen and learn.

So the workmen came back again. But this
time they were not here to make me bigger or more
beautiful. No, they took away my organ, pipe by pipe.
They packed candles and incense, prayer books and
chalices tightly into boxes. They wrapped my statues in
crinkly paper and soft blankets and carried them down
my aisle. And then they locked my door behind them.

I was a church, all alone.

What was to become of me?

I did not have to wonder for long. All around me, the neighborhood was noisy and crowded. Children laughed, horses clop-clopped, and peddlers sold their wares.

"Pickles here, get your fresh pickles!" "Plump live chickens here, best in town!"

Newcomers arrived from across the ocean. They hurried past, their belongings tied up in cloth bags slung over their shoulders.

A group of those newcomers sailed across the ocean from Ukraine. They opened up my front door, looked around, and decided to stay.

Gone were the altar and the incense, the statues and the steeple. The new families filled my ritual baths with water. Carefully, they placed the Torah scrolls in a brand new ark. Best of all, they painted colorful pictures on my ceiling.

These Jewish families called themselves Shomrei Mishmeres. Now they had their own place to gather and pray, study and sing, listen and learn.

I was a synagogue, once again.

Downstairs, my new families built a big oven, brick by brick. Every spring they heated that oven, and its fire warmed my insides.

When the oven was very hot, Aaron and Isidor carefully mixed flour and water. Quickly, quickly, their mothers and aunts rolled the dough out flat. Singing and praying, their fathers and grandfathers slid it into the oven with big wooden paddles.

One minute, two minutes, three, and out came crispy brown-flecked matzohs, unleavened bread to eat during the Passover holiday.

How I loved my new children. Outside on my steps, Lina and Esther played with their dolls. Harry and Seymour built pyramids of nuts and then—*crack, crash, crunch*—knocked them down. Inside, their mothers listened as their fathers prayed.

My pews were filled with people, and I was filled with joy.

One day, a parade came around the corner. Men
sang, women laughed, children skipped and hid,
jumped and ran. Dogs barked. Something, someone
was coming down the street. It was a bearded man,
held high in a big leather chair! The families were
carrying their rabbi in a seat of honor.

When they reached my front steps they set
him down carefully and, beaming, he stood
up and nodded to the families.

And then they went inside and prayed:

"*Baruch ata Adonai …*"

"Blessed are you, O, Lord …"

What a joyous day that was.

How I wished things had stayed that way.

But slowly, slowly, my pews grew emptier. Aaron and Esther, Harry and Lina grew up and had families of their own. But they did not come back to visit me. They had moved away, to new neighborhoods of neat houses with green lawns and smooth black streets.

The people who stayed behind tried to take care of me, but they were becoming tired and frail, stooped and gray.

I was a synagogue, growing old. What was to become of me?

One day, some men gathered in my basement to hold a meeting.

"There is no money to fix the leaking roof or patch the cracking walls."

"All the young people have moved away."

"We have no choice but to leave our old building."

"But they will tear it down and make a parking lot!"

Could it be true? Through good times and bad, I had sheltered my families as they gathered and prayed, studied and sang, listened and learned.

Was this really the end for me?

And then the workmen came back. I braced myself for the first blow, for surely they were here to tear me down, brick by brick.

But, no, they came with shovel and pail, hammer and nail, brick and stone to fix me once again. They used big steel beams to strengthen my roof and straighten my walls. They repaired my windows and polished my pews. And when I was sparkling top to bottom, there was a big celebration.

Women in fancy dresses and men in crisp suits and ties filled my pews. The mayor talked about how important I was, and how handsome. My fresh white walls gleamed and my new carpet was soft under people's feet. As I listened to those speeches, I was filled with pride.

I was a museum, and I felt brand new.

But something was missing.

What could it be?

The next morning, I heard it: the laughter of children. A group of students was climbing my front steps. David and Steven jostled and joked, and Susan giggled as Karen told her a secret. And then their teacher opened my big front doors.

One by one, the children stepped inside and looked around. They walked downstairs and back up. They sat down and looked up at my stained glass window with its colorful Star of David. They wondered and smiled and joked and learned.

I am very old now, but almost every day, children like Toby and Tanesha, Katelyn and Kyle, come to visit me.

Their laughter makes me feel young again, and I am filled with joy.

The Lloyd Street Synagogue

The Lloyd Street Synagogue, built in 1845, is today the third oldest synagogue building in the United States. It has been home to three congregations.

1845—1889   Baltimore Hebrew Congregation

1889—1905   St. John the Baptist Lithuanian Catholic Church

1905—1960   Congregation Shomrei Mishmeres Ha-Kodesh (Guardians of the Holy Sanctuary)

Since 1963, the Jewish Museum of Maryland has owned and operated the Lloyd Street Synagogue as an historic site. To find out more about the synagogue or to plan your visit, please go to www.jewishmuseummd.org.

SYNAGOGUE,
Lloyd Street.

Lloyd Street Synagogue, 1864. Courtesy of the Ross J. Kelbaugh Collection, 1997.71.1.